# HORRID HENRY'S BIGGEST AND BEST EVER JOKE BOOK

**Francesca Simon** spent her childhood in California, and then went to Yale and Oxford Universities to study medieval history and literature. She now lives in London with her family. She has written over fifty books and won the Children's Book Of The Year in 2008 at the Galaxy British Book Awards for *Horrid Henry And The Abominable Snowman.*

**Tony Ross** is one of Britain's best known illustrators, with many picture books to his name. He has also produced the line drawings for many fiction titles, for authors such as David Walliams, Jeanne Willis, Enid Blyton, Astrid Lindgren, and many more. He lives in Wales.

Also by Francesca Simon

*Don't Cook Cinderella*
*Helping Hercules*

and for younger readers

*Don't be Horrid, Henry*
*The Parent Swap Shop*
*Spider School*
*The Topsy-Turvies*

For a complete list of **Horrid Henry** titles, visit
www.horridhenry.co.uk
or
www.orionbooks.co.uk

# HORRID HENRY'S BIGGEST AND BEST EVER JOKE BOOK

Francesca Simon
*Illustrated by* Tony Ross

Orion
Children's Books

This collection first published in Great Britain in 2014
by Orion Children's Books
a division of the Orion Publishing Group Ltd
Orion House
5 Upper St Martin's Lane
London WC2H 9EA
An Hachette UK company

1 3 5 7 9 10 8 6 4 2



The Orion Publishing Group's policy is to use papers that are natural, renewable and recyclable products and made from wood grown in sustainable forests. The logging and manufacturing processes are expected to conform to the environmental regulations of the country of origin.

A catalogue record for this book is available from the British Library.

ISBN 978 1 4440 1174 6

Printed in Great Britain by Clays Ltd, St Ives plc

www.horridhenry.co.uk
www.orionbooks.co.uk

# CONTENTS

# HORRID HENRY'S JOKE BOOK

**To the children of
Yerbury Primary School,
who told Henry
such brilliant jokes**

# CONTENTS

# Warning!

Do not read this joke book if:

☠ Your name is Prissy Polly
☠ You're a goody-goody, ugly toad, tattle-tale
☠ You watch Nellie's Nursery on TV

These jokes are horrid. These jokes are guaranteed to make horrible little brothers feel sick and parents run screaming from the room. These jokes are so rude and so gross that –

'Oy! Peter! Stop reading right now. I said, put down my book – or else. These gross-out jokes are not for little toads!'

'Muuum! Henry's being mean to me!'

'Don't be horrid, Henry. Let Peter read your jokes.'

'NO!'

# MUMMY'S CURSE JOKES

*Why didn't the skeleton and the monster fight?*
The skeleton didn't have the guts.

*Why was the Egyptian boy upset?*
His daddy was a mummy.

*During which age did mummies live?*
The Band-age.

*What does a monster mummy say to her kids at lunch?*
Don't talk with someone in your mouth.

*What did the metal monster want written on his gravestone?*
Rust in piece.

*What pets does Dracula own?*
A bloodhound and a ghoulfish.

*What is sung in the vampire production of Abba hits?*
Fang you for the music.

*Who works in monster hospitals?*
A skeleton staff.

*What feature do witches love having on their computers?*
A spell checker.

*What should you do after shaking hands with a monster?*
Count your fingers.

*When a vampire drinks too much, what does it get?*
A fangover.

*What did the vampire crawling through the desert say?*
'Blood! Blood!'

*What do vampires cross the sea in?*
Blood vessels.

*Which monster ate the three bears' porridge?*
Ghouldilocks.

*What do you call a ghostly teddy bear?*
Winnie the OOOOOHhhhhhhh.

*What haircut do monsters like?*
Deadlocks.

*What did the pirate get when he hit the skeleton?*
A skull and very cross bones.

*Why didn't the skeleton go to the party?*
He had nobody to go with.

*Where do skeletons swim?*
The Dead Sea.

**BOY**: Mummy, Mummy, Ralph just called me a werewolf.
**MUM**: Shut up and comb your face.

*Why are zombies never lonely?*
They can always dig up a few friends.

*What do you get if a huge, hairy monster steps on Batman and Robin?*
Flatman and Ribbon

**HANGMAN**: Do you have a last request?
**PRISONER**: Yes, can I sing a song?
**HANGMAN**: All right. Just one.
**PRISONER**: Ten million green bottles, standing on a wall . . .

*Why is the letter V like a monster?*
It comes after U.

*What did the monster say to his daughter?*
'You're the apple of my eye eye eye eye.'

*What is a monster's favourite game?*
Hide and shriek.

*What should you say if you meet a ghost?*
How do you boo?

*What do little ghosts drink?*
Evaporated milk.

*When do ghosts usually appear?*
Just before someone screams.

*What would you find on a haunted beach?*
A sandwitch.

*What do short-sighted ghosts wear?*
Spooktacles.

*Why did the mummy have no friends?*
He was too wrapped up in himself.

*Where do ghosts go on holiday?*
Death Valley.

# GRISLY GRUB JOKES

**BELCH! CRUNCH! OOZE! SPLAT! Ha ha ha. These are great jokes to tell when you want to make people feel sick.**

VAMPIRE TO SON: You're late. We had guests for dinner. They were delicious!

*What do cannibals like for breakfast?*
Buttered host.

*What does Dracula like for breakfast?*
Ready neck.

*What do monsters call knights in armour?*
Tinned food.

*What do monsters make with cars?*
Traffic jam.

*What do cannibals play at parties?*
Swallow the leader.

*What does a sea-monster eat for dinner?*
Fish and ships.

*How do monsters have their eggs?*
Terrifried.

*What's the difference between school dinners and slugs?*

School dinners come on plates.

*What do you call someone who puts poison on their breakfast?*
A cereal killer.

*What do mermaids have on toast?*
Mermalade.

*Why did the man drown in his muesli?*
He was pulled under by a strong currant.

*What's yellow and dangerous?*
Shark-infested custard.

*What do you get if you cross an egg with a barrel of gunpowder?*
A boom-meringue.

*Waiter! Waiter! This egg is bad.*
Don't blame me, I only laid the table.

*Waiter! Waiter! There's a fly in my soup.*
I'm sorry, sir, the dog must have missed it.

**HENRY**: Why is your thumb on my sandwich?

**DEMON DINNER LADY**: To stop it falling on the floor again.

*What's worse than finding a caterpillar in your apple?*
Finding half a caterpillar in your apple.

*Why don't cannibals eat clowns?*
Because they taste funny.

*What do French pupils say after finishing school dinners?*
Mercy.

*What happened to the butcher who backed into a meat grinder?*
He got a little behind in his work.

**Henry**: What's yellow, brown and hairy?
**Peter**: I don't know.
**Henry**: Cheese on toast stuck to the carpet.

*Waiter! Waiter! Your thumb is in my soup.*
Don't worry. It's not hot.

*What do you give a cannibal who's late for dinner?*
The cold shoulder.

*What's yellow, flat and flies around the kitchen?*
An unidentified flying omelette.

*What's the worst thing you'll find in a school canteen?*
The food.

**Miss Battle-Axe**: Henry, how many bones have you got in your body?
**Henry**: It feels like 4,000. I had fish for school dinner.

# GROSS-OUT JOKES

*What happens when a baby eats Rice Krispies?*
It goes snap, crackle and poop.

*Why is your mouth all fluffy?*
My mum hoovered up my toffee.

*What do you get if you sit under a cow?*
A pat on the head.

*What monster do you get at the end of your finger?*
A bogey monster.

*Waiter! Waiter! There's a fly in my soup.*
Quiet or everyone will want one.

*What's green and hangs from trees?*
Giraffe snot.

*What do you give sea-sick elephants?*
Plenty of room.

*What's an ig?*
An Eskimo's house without a toilet.

*What's an insect's best chat-up line?*
'Is this stool taken?'

*What goes ha-ha-bonk?*
A man laughing his head off.

*Why did the sand scream?*
The sea weed.

*What do you do when your nose goes on strike?*
Picket.

*How do you make a tissue dance?*
Put a little boogie in it.

Knock knock.
Who's there?
Alec.
Alec who?
Alec to pick my nose.

Knock knock.
Who's there?
Ahab.
Ahab who?
Ahab to go to the loo.

*What's brown and sticky?*
A brown stick.

# BOGEY BABYSITTER JOKES

**Warning! Make sure you can make a quick getaway if you tell a rabid babysitter any of these jokes. Believe me, I know.**

HENRY: Rebecca, you remind me of a movie star.

RABID REBECCA: Oooh. Which one?

HENRY: The Incredible Hulk.

**Rabid Rebecca**: I always speak my mind.
**Henry**: I'm surprised you have so much to say then.

**Rabid Rebecca**: Whenever I'm down in the dumps, I buy myself a new T-shirt.
**Henry**: So *that's* where you get them.

**Henry**: Why do I have to go to bed?
**Rebecca**: Because the bed won't come to you.

**Rebecca**: How long can someone live without a brain?
**Henry**: How old are you?

*Did you hear about the babysitter who accidentally plugged her electric blanket into the toaster?*

She spent the night popping out of bed.

**Nah nah ne nah nah**

# TERMINATOR GLADIATOR JOKES

**If you want to make your mean, horrible parents really scream, just tell them one of these jokes.**

*What do you call a sheep with a machine gun?*
Lambo.

*What's got four legs and an arm?*
A Rottweiler.

*What do you call a budgie that's been run over by a lawn mower?*
Shredded tweet.

*What did the fly say as it hit the windscreen?*
That's me all over.

*What's the last thing that goes through a wasp's mind when it hits a windscreen?*
Its sting.

*What's green and red and goes round and round?*
A frog in a blender.

*What do you call a cow with no legs?*
Ground beef.

*Why did the hedgehog cross the road?*
To see his flatmate.

*Did you hear about the man who had a dog with no legs?*
He took it for a drag every day.

*How do you kill a circus?*
Go for the juggler.

# UNDERPANTS JOKES

**Boy oh boy! Jokes do not get more horrid than these.**

*What's hairy, scary and wears its knickers on its head?*
The Underwere-wolf.

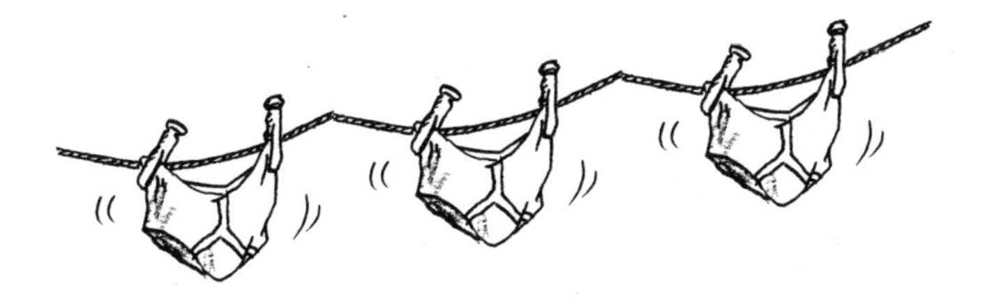

*What are two robbers called?*
A pair of nickers.

*Why do werewolves have holes in their underpants?*
So furry tails can come true.

*What gushes out of the ground shouting, 'Knickers, knickers'?*
Crude oil.

*What gushes out of the ground shouting, 'Underwear, underwear'?*
Refined oil.

*What hangs out your underpants?*
Your mum.

*Why did the golfer wear two pairs of pants?*
In case he got a hole in one.

*What's the best way to make pants last?*
Make vests first.

Knock knock.
Who's there?
Nicholas.
Nicholas who?
Nicholas girls shouldn't climb trees.

*What goes 300mph on a washing line?*
Honda pants.

*What do you get if you pull your underwear up to your neck?*
A chest of drawers.

**Mini Minnie**: Do you know how old Miss Battle-Axe is?

**Lisping Lilly**: No, but I know how to find out. Take off her knickers!

**Mini Minnie**: Take off her knickers! How will that tell us?

**Lisping Lilly**: Well, in my knickers it says, '3 to 5 years'.

# STINKBOMBS

**Hold your nose for these stinkers!**

*What did the skunk say when the wind blew in the opposite direction?*
It's all coming back to me now.

*What do you get if you cross a bear with a skunk?*
Winnie the Poo.

*How do you stop someone who's been working out in the gym on a hot day from smelling?*
Put a peg on his nose.

*Why do giraffes have long necks?*
Their feet smell.

*What did one burp say to the other?*
Let's be stinkers and sneak out the other end.
**(Ralph's favourite joke)**

*What happens when you play table tennis with a rotten egg?*
First it goes ping, then it goes pong.

*What's brown and sits on a piano stool?*
Beethoven's last movement.

*What do you get if you cross a skunk with a cuckoo?*
A bird that stinks and doesn't give a hoot.

*What do you call a flying skunk?*
A smellicopter.

*What's the hairiest, smelliest thing on earth* **(besides Peter)***?*
King Pong.

# DOCTOR DETTOL JOKES

**Next time a doctor tries to give you an injection, distract her with a few of these goodies.**

*Doctor, Doctor, I think I'm a pair of curtains.*
Well, pull yourself together.

*Did you hear about the man who swallowed some Christmas decorations?*
He got tinselitis.

*Doctor, Doctor, what's a good cure for snake bites?*
Stop biting so many snakes.

*What did the vampire doctor say to his patients?*
Necks please.

*Doctor, Doctor, can you give me something for wind?*
Sure, take this kite.

*When is the best time to visit the dentist?*
Tooth-hurty.

*Doctor, Doctor, people keep ignoring me.*
Who said that?

*What is the most common illness in China?*
Kung flu.

*Doctor, Doctor, you have to help me out.*
Which way did you come in?

*Doctor, Doctor, I feel as if I'm getting smaller.*
You'll just have to be a little patient.

*Doctor, Doctor, there's something wrong with my tummy.*
Keep your jumper on and nobody will notice.

A girl walks into the doctor's office. She has a banana in her left ear and a carrot in her right. There's a piece of celery in one nostril and a small potato in the other.

'Doctor, I feel terrible,' she says.

'Well, your problem is obvious,' says the doctor. 'You're clearly not eating properly.'

*Doctor Doctor, I keep thinking I'm a bell.*
Take this medicine and, if it doesn't work, give me a ring.

*Doctor, Doctor, I feel like a biscuit.*
You must be crackers.

*Doctor, Doctor, I've just swallowed a roll of film.*
Sit in the sunshine and hope that nothing develops.

*Doctor, Doctor, I think I need glasses.*
You certainly do, sir. This is a flower shop.

*Doctor, Doctor, I keep seeing insects spinning.*
Don't worry. It's just a bug that's going round.

# DIZZY DAVE'S DINOSAUR JOKES

**Dave paid me £1, so I let him add a few dinosaur jokes to my book.**

*What do you call a dinosaur with one eye?*
Do-you-think-he-saur-us.

*Why did the dinosaur cross the road?*
There weren't any chickens in those days.

*How do you stop a dinosaur charging?*
Take away his credit card.

*What do you call a dinosaur with a banana in each ear?*
Anything you like. He can't hear you.

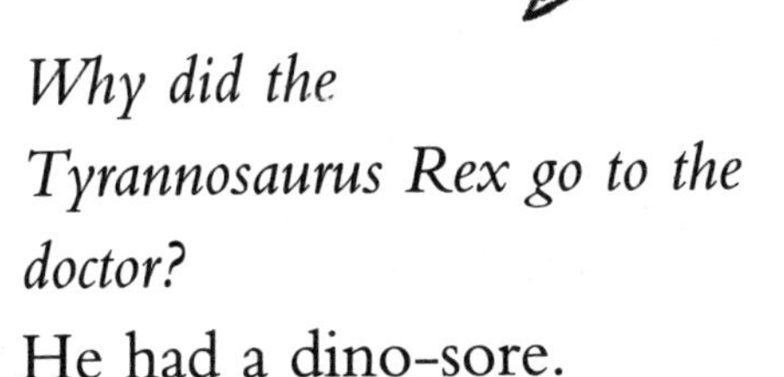

*Why did the Tyrannosaurus Rex go to the doctor?*
He had a dino-sore.

*What do you get when dinosaurs crash their cars?*
Tyrannosaurus wrecks.

*What do you call it when a Tyrannosaurus Rex gets the ball into the back of the net?*
A dino-score.

*What do you get when you cross a Tyrannosaurus Rex with fireworks?*
Dino-mite.

*What was the scariest prehistoric animal?*
The Terror-dactyl.

*What did dinosaurs have that no other animals ever had?*
Baby dinosaurs.

*What do you call a Tyrannosaurus Rex that sleeps all day?*
A dino-snore.

*Why do Tyrannosaurus Rex like to eat snowmen?*
They melt in their mouths.

*What's huge and bumps into mountains?*
A dinosaur playing blind man's buff.

*What do you call a dinosaur with no head?*
A Tyrannosaurus Nex.

*What do you get if you cross a dinosaur with a pig?*
Jurassic Pork.

*How can you tell if a dinosaur is a vegetarian?*
Lie down on a plate.

*Why did the Tyrannosaurus Rex cross the road?*
So he could eat the chickens on the other side.

# MOODY MARGARET KNOCKS SOUR SUSAN JOKES

**The only good thing about living next door to Moody Margaret is that she knows some good jokes. There's just one problem . . .**

MARGARET: Knock Knock.
SUSAN: Who's there?
MARGARET: Little old lady.
SUSAN: Little old lady who?
MARGARET (yodelling): Little old lady ooooh.

MARGARET: Knock Knock.
SUSAN: Who's there?
MARGARET: Abyssinia.
SUSAN: Abyssinia who?
MARGARET: Abyssinia when I get back.

MARGARET: Knock Knock.
SUSAN: Who's there?
MARGARET: Canoe.
SUSAN: Canoe who?
MARGARET: Canoe open the door? It's cold out here.

**Margaret**: Knock Knock.
**Susan**: Who's there?
**Margaret**: Bella.
**Susan**: Bella who?
**Margaret**: Bella bottom trousers.

**Margaret**: Knock Knock.
**Susan**: Who's there?
**Margaret**: Dishes.
**Susan**: Dishes who?
**Margaret**: Dishes your friend. Let me in.

**Margaret**: Knock knock.
**Susan**: Who's there?
**Margaret**: Lettuce.
**Susan**: Lettuce who?
**Margaret**: Lettuce in, it's raining.

**Margaret**: Knock knock.
**Susan**: Who's there?
**Margaret**: Sorry.
**Susan**: Sorry who?
**Margaret**: Sorry, wrong door.

**Margaret**: Knock knock.
**Susan**: Who's there?
**Margaret**: Boo.
**Susan**: Boo who?
**Margaret**: Don't cry, it's only a joke.

**Margaret**: Knock knock.
**Susan**: Who's there?
**Margaret**: Abby.
**Susan**: Abby who?
**Margaret**: Abby stung me on the bottom.

**MARGARET**: Knock knock.
**SUSAN**: Who's there?
**MARGARET**: Nun.
**SUSAN**: Nun who?
**MARGARET**: Nun of your business.

**MARGARET**: Knock knock.
**SUSAN**: Who's there?
**MARGARET**: Germaine.
**SUSAN**: Germaine who?
**MARGARET**: Germaine you don't recognise me?

**MARGARET**: Knock knock.
**SUSAN**: Who's there?
**MARGARET**: Ron.
**SUSAN**: Ron who?
**MARGARET**: Ron as fast as you can!

MARGARET: Knock knock.
SUSAN: Who's there?
MARGARET: Ada.
SUSAN: Ada who?
MARGARET: Ada lot of breakfast and I'm stuffed.

MARGARET: Knock knock.
SUSAN: Who's there?
MARGARET: Cows go.
SUSAN: Cows go who?
MARGARET: No they don't, they go moo.

MARGARET: Knock knock.
SUSAN: Who's there?
MARGARET: Adjust.
SUSAN: Adjust who?
MARGARET: Adjust made a mess on the floor.

**I couldn't steal any more of their jokes because . . . Aarrrggghhh! I'm getting out of here!**

**'How come you always get to go first?' said Susan sourly.**

**'Because you can't tell jokes and I can,' said Margaret.**

**'I can too tell jokes!'**

**'Can't!'**

**'Can!'**

**SLAP!**

**SLAP!**

# BEEFY BERT'S BEASTLY JOKES

**HENRY: Bert, why did the chicken cross the road?**

**BERT: I dunno.**

**HENRY: There's no point telling you jokes, Bert! Why do you always answer, 'I dunno'?**

**BERT: I dunno.**

*What do you get if you cross a centipede with a parrot?*
A walkie-talkie.

*What do you call a sheep with no legs?*
A cloud.

*Why do ducks have webbed feet?*
To stamp out forest fires.

*Why do elephants have*
*big, flat feet?*
To stamp out flaming ducks.

*What goes 99-clonk, 99-clonk, 99-clonk?*
A centipede with a wooden leg.

*How do you hire a horse?*
Put a brick under each hoof.

*What's worse than an alligator with toothache?*
A centipede with athlete's foot.

*How do you know which end of a worm is its head?*
Tickle it and see which end smiles.

*What has 50 legs but can't walk?*
Half a centipede.

*What has four wheels and flies?*
A rubbish bin.

*What did the slug say as he slipped down the wall?*
How slime flies.

*Why did the turkey cross the road?*
It was the chicken's day off.

*How do you know when there's an elephant under your bed?*
Your nose touches the ceiling.

*What's grey and squirts jam at you?*
A mouse eating a doughnut.

*What did the teddy bear say when he was offered dessert?*
No thanks, I'm stuffed.

*How does an elephant get up a tree?*
Sits on an acorn and waits for it to grow.

*How does an elephant get down from a tree?*
Sits on a leaf and waits for it to fall.

*What's black and white and red all over?*
A zebra in a phone box.

*Where do frogs keep their money?*
In riverbanks.

*How long should a giraffe's legs be?*
Long enough to touch the ground.

*What's a chicken's favourite TV programme?*
The feather forecast.

*Why do mice need oiling?*
They squeak.

*What bird is always out of breath?*
A puffin.

*What do you call a carton of ducks?*
A box of quackers.

*What's a frog's favourite drink?*
Croak-a-Cola.

*What do you call a crocodile at the North Pole?*
Lost.

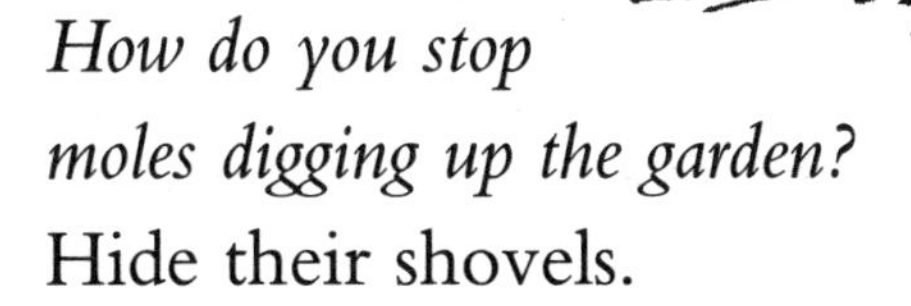

*How do you stop moles digging up the garden?*
Hide their shovels.

*What do you call a fly with no wings?*
A walk.

An elephant is walking through the jungle when he sees a turtle sitting by a log.

'Hey,' says the elephant, 'you're the turtle that bit me 57 years ago.'

'How on earth do you remember that?' asks the turtle.

'Easy,' says the elephant, 'I've got turtle recall.'

# AEROBIC AL'S SPORTS JOKES

**I hate PE! I hate Sports Day, too, unless of course I win everything. But Al promised to pick me ahead of Margaret for football today if I let him put some jokes in my book. It'll be worth it just to see the look on Margaret's grumpy, misery-gut face!**

*Why is Cinderella bad at football?*
She has a pumpkin as her coach.

*Why was Cinderella knocked out of the football team?*
She kept running away from the ball.

*What did one earwig say to the other earwig as they fell out of a tree?*
Earwig go, earwig go, earwig go.

*Where do footballers dance?*
At a football.

*Why don't grasshoppers go to football games?*
They prefer cricket matches.

*What football team*
*does King Kong support?*
Aston Gorilla.

*Why were the flies playing*
*football in a saucer?*
They were practising for
the cup.

*What's an insect's favourite game?*
Cricket.

*Why couldn't the car play football?*
It had only one boot.

*Why did the basketball player go to the doctor?*
To get more shots.

*What is a goal-keeper's favourite snack?*
Beans on post.

*How did the basketball court get wet?*
The players dribbled all over it.

*What do you call a cat that plays football?*
Puss in boots.

*Why do elephants have grey trunks?*
They're all on the same swimming team.

*How did the football pitch become a triangle?*
Somebody took a corner.

*Why should Sports Days never be held in the jungle?*
There are too many cheetahs.

*Why wasn't the footballer invited to dinner?*
He dribbled too much.

*Why didn't the dog like swimming?*
It was a boxer.

*What part of a swimming pool is never the same?*
The changing rooms.

*Where do old bowling balls end up?*
The gutter.

*What happened when two balls of string had a race?*
It ended in a tie.

*What's Aerobic Al's favourite subject in school?*
Jog-graphy.

# JOKES NOT TO TELL AUNT RUBY

Not Suitable for Aunts

**MUM: Henry! I've just had the strangest call from Aunt Ruby. . .**
**HENRY: Hide!**

*What do you call an aunt on the toilet?*
Lou Lou.

*What do you call an aunt who falls off the toilet?*
Lou Roll.

*Why do you put your aunt in the fridge?*
To make Auntie-freeze.

*Has your aunt caught up with you yet?*
No, but when she does I'm going to need a lot of Auntie-septic.

*How do you make anti-freeze?*
Hide her nightie.

*How can you tell if Aunt Ruby's been to visit?*
She's still in the house.

**Mum**: Henry, we're having Aunt Ruby for lunch this Sunday.
**Henry**: Can't we have roast beef instead?

**Mum**: Henry! Why did you put a slug in Aunt Ruby's bed?

**Henry**: I couldn't find a snake.

**Aunt Ruby**: Goodness! It's raining cats and dogs.

**Henry**: I know. I nearly stepped in a poodle.

**Aunt Ruby**: Well, Henry, I'm leaving tomorrow. Are you sorry?

**Henry**: Oh yes, Aunt Ruby, I thought you were leaving today.

# JOKES NOT TO TELL MISS BATTLE-AXE

**These jokes are guaranteed to send teachers screaming from the classroom. Just don't blame me if you get sent to the Head . . .**

*What did the inflatable teacher say to the inflatable boy who brought a pin to the inflatable school?*
You've let me down, you've let the school down, but worst of all, you've let yourself down.

**MISS BATTLE-AXE**: Henry! What is glue made out of?
**HENRY**: Um . . . sticks.

**MISS BATTLE-AXE**: Henry! Were you copying Susan's sums?
**HENRY**: No! I was just seeing if she'd got mine right.

**HENRY**: Would you blame someone for something they hadn't done?
**MISS BATTLE-AXE**: Of course not.
**HENRY**: Good, I haven't done my homework.

**Miss Battle-Axe**: Henry, I hope I didn't see you copying Clare.
**Henry**: I hope you didn't either.

**Miss Battle-Axe**: Linda! Why are you late for school again?
**Lazy Linda**: I overslept.
**Miss Battle-Axe**: You mean you sleep at home as well?

*What would you get if you crossed Miss Battle-Axe with a vampire?*
Lots of blood tests.

**MISS BATTLE-AXE**: William! You've put your shoes on the wrong feet.
**WEEPY WILLIAM**: Waaaah! But these are the only feet I've got.

**MISS BATTLE-AXE**: Henry! You missed school yesterday, didn't you?
**HENRY**: Not very much.

**MISS BATTLE-AXE**: Henry! If you multiplied 1497 by 371 what answer would you get?
**HENRY**: The wrong one.

**Miss Battle-Axe**: Henry, where are the Kings and Queens of England crowned?
**Henry**: On their heads.

**Miss Battle-Axe**: Henry, make up a sentence with the word 'lettuce' in it.
**Henry**: Let us out of school early.

*What's the difference between homework and an onion?*
Nobody cries when you cut up homework.

**Miss Battle-Axe**: Henry! I'm sending you off the football pitch.

**Henry**: What for?

**Miss Battle-Axe**: The rest of the match.

**Miss Battle-Axe**: Henry, what is a mushroom?

**Henry**: The place where they make school dinners.

*Did you hear about the cross-eyed teacher?*

He couldn't control his pupils.

**MISS BATTLE-AXE**: Henry! Why are you doing a headstand in the classroom?
**HENRY**: You said we should turn things over in our minds.

**HENRY**: I wish we lived in the olden days.
**RALPH**: Why?
**HENRY**: We wouldn't have so much history to learn.

**MISS BATTLE-AXE**: Henry, I do wish you'd pay a little attention.
**HENRY**: Believe me, I'm paying as little as I can.

**Miss Battle-Axe**: That's the most horrid boy in the whole school.

**Mum**: That's my son.

**Miss Battle-Axe**: Oh, I'm so sorry.

**Mum**: *You're* sorry?

# PERFECT PETER'S FAVOURITE JOKES

'NO! I don't want Peter's stupid, smelly jokes in my joke book.'

'Don't be horrid, Henry!'

'I DON'T WANT PETER'S STUPID, BABY JOKES IN MY BOOK.

AND THAT'S FINAL.'

'Henry, I'm warning you . . .'

'NOOOOOOOO!'

'That's it, Henry. No TV for a week.'

'Oh all right. He can put in his stupid, yucky jokes.'

Psst. Listen, everyone, don't read them. They're awful. Skip ahead to the next section.

*What's green and rides a horse?*
Alexander the Grape.

**I thought I said, don't read Peter's dumb jokes!**

*What do you call a sheep on a trampoline?*
A woolly jumper.

*What happens if you fall asleep under a car?*
You wake up oily in the morning.

**Told you they were awful! Now stop reading!**

*Why couldn't the sailor play cards?*
The captain was standing on the deck.

*How do chickens dance?*
Chick to chick.

**Groan.**

*Why did the man with one hand cross the road?*
To get to the second hand shop.

*Why did the germ cross the microscope?*
To get to the other slide.

*What do you get if you dial 666?*
The Australian police.

*How do you use an Egyptian doorbell?*
Just toot-and-come-in.

*What's orange and sounds like a parrot?*
A carrot.

*What do you get if you pour hot water down a rabbit hole?*
Hot cross bunnies.

**You still here? Then it's your own fault if you have to read dumb bunny jokes.**

*What do you call a blind reindeer?*
No eye deer.

*Why did the elephant cross the road?*
The chicken was on holiday.

**'Peter! That's my joke. I already told it.'**
**'It's my joke! You stole it.'**
**'Didn't.'**
**'Did.'**
**'MUMMMMMMMMMM!'**

*Why did the bubblegum cross the road?*
It was stuck to the chicken's foot.

*What do you call a man who's been buried in a bog for 4000 years?*
Pete.

*What do you call a priest on a motorbike?*
Rev.

*Where do frogs hang their coats?*
In a croakroom.

**Peter! That's the worst joke I've ever heard. Cross it out this minute.**

*What did the policeman say to his belly?*
'You're under a vest.'

*What's seven feet tall, green, and sits in the corner?*
The Incredible Sulk.

*What do you call a bear without an ear?*
B.

**Only an ugly, smelly toad would find that funny.**

*What does the Spanish farmer say to his chickens?*
'Oh lay!'

*What did the martian say to the petrol pump?*
Take your finger out of your ear when I'm talking to you.

*When is a tractor not a tractor?*
When it turns into a field.

**When I'm king, anyone who tells any of Peter's stupid jokes will get trampled on by elephants. I mean it!**

*How do you know flowers are lazy?*
You always find them in beds.

*What happens when you drop a green rock in the Red Sea?*
It gets wet.

**Aaarrrgghhh.**

*Which pet makes the most noise?*
A trum-pet.

**They're finished. Phew. That was horrible. I'm going to glue those pages together so no one will ever have to suffer again.**

# JOKES MUCH TOO RUDE TO TELL MUM

**Yes! Now some real jokes.**

*What did the constipated mathematician do?*
He got a pencil and worked it out.

*What jumps out from behind a snowdrift and shows you his bottom?*
The A-bum-inable snowman.

If a centipede a pint and a millipede a litre, how much can a precipice?

A little girl wet herself in class and the teacher asked her why she didn't put up her hand.

'I did, Miss, but it ran through my fingers.'

*If you're American when you go into the toilet and American when you come out of the toilet, what are you when you're in the toilet?*
European.

*What did the doctor say to the man wearing cling-film?*
'I can clearly see you're nuts.'

Knock Knock.
Who's there?
Madam.
Madam who?
Madam fingers are stuck in the keyhole!

Knock Knock!
Who's there?
Done up.
Done up who?
You did a poo?!

Did you hear about the cannibal who passed his cousin in the woods?

*What did the elephant say to the naked man?*
'You can't pick up —'

**'Henry! That's enough! Go to your room!'**

KRUNCH

# HORRID HENRY'S JOLLY JOKE BOOK

*Acknowledgements*

Many thanks to the children of Avondale Park Primary School and High Ham School, who told me some great jokes. And special thanks to Charlotte Mendelson for the "interrupting sheep" joke, and to Kate Ballard.

# CONTENTS

# HORRID HENRY'S JOLLY JOKE BOOK

Bleeeeeeecccchhhh! What a bunch of copycats! Miss Battle-Axe said everyone in the school could put their best jokes in this new joke book, and the person with the best one would get a really, really great prize. Whoopee! Well, let them try to out-joke me. My Purple Hand Pirate jokes are sure to be the best. Margaret wouldn't know a good joke if it banged her over the head. And as for Peter – no way is he wrecking this book with his stupid worm toad jokes.

Henry, this is a school joke book and I have just as much right to put in my jokes as you do.

**Says who?**

Says Miss Lovely.

**We'll see about that. I'm the boss and what I say goes.**

Oh Yeah? Says who?

**Says me, Margaret, you old pants face.**

No one made you boss, Henry. And your jokes are stupid.

**Not as stupid as yours. Vote Henry! Vote Henry! Vote Henry!**

# FIONA'S FIERY FANGMANGLER JOKES

**NO! Vote Henry!!**

Shut up, Henry.

**Shut up yourself!**

*What's a shark's favourite game?*
Bite and seek.

*Why didn't the skeleton go swimming?*
Because he had no body to go with.

*What do devils drink?*
Demonade.

*What's a monster's favourite soup?*
Scream of tomato.

*What did one cool ghost say to the other?*
Get a life, dude.

*Who is green and eats porridge?*
Mouldy Locks.

*What did the cannibal say when he came home and found his mum chopping up a python and a pygmy?*
'Oh no, not snake and pygmy pie again!'

*Why should you stay calm when you meet a cannibal?*
Because it's no good getting in a stew.

*What does a cannibal call a phone book?*
A menu.

*Why did the cannibal go to the wedding reception?*
So he could toast the guests.

*What did the cannibal say when he saw Graham asleep?*
'Aaaaah! Breakfast in bed.'

**Pssst! Everyone. Just skip ahead to my pirate jokes! Vote Henry!**

# ANDREW'S ANXIOUS JOKES

I don't suppose anyone will vote for any of my jokes ...

*What do you call an anxious dinosaur?*
A nervous rex.

**Psychiatrist:** What's your problem?
**Patient:** I think I'm a chicken.
**Psychiatrist:** How long has this been going on?
**Patient:** Ever since I was an egg.

*What's the worst vegetable to have on a boat?*
A leek.

*What lies at the bottom of the ocean and twitches?*
A nervous wreck.

# GURINDER'S GORGEOUS JOKES

I'm the most beautiful girl in the class, so I deserve to win.

**Yeah, right, Gurinder. Not!**

GURINDER: I spend hours in front of the mirror admiring myself. Do you think that's vanity?
MARGARET: No, imagination.

**MARGARET**: My beauty is timeless.
**GURINDER**: Yeah, it could stop a clock.

**GURINDER**: Will I lose my looks when I get older?
**MARGARET**: With luck, yes.

A blonde was walking down the road with a piglet under her arm.
As she passed the school, someone asked: 'Where did you get that?'
'I won her in a raffle!' replied the piglet.

*Why was the girl named Sugar?*
Because she was so refined.

*How does a blonde kill a fish?*
She drowns it.

Did you hear about the blonde tap dancer?
She fell in the sink.

*What did Snow White say while she waited for her photos?*
Some day my prints will come.

*What did the stamp say to the envelope on Valentine's Day?*
I'm stuck on you.

*What did one magnet say to the other magnet?*
I find you very attractive.

*What do you call a girl with sausages on her head?*
Barbie.

*I don't think these photographs you've taken do me justice.*
You don't want justice – you want mercy.

**NICK**: Do you think my sister Lily is pretty?
**HENRY**: Well, let's just say if you pulled her pigtail she'd probably say 'oink, oink.'

Vote Gurinder!

# MARGARET'S MOODY JOKES

**I think I'll help Margaret with a few jokes . . .**

*What's the difference between Margaret and a cow?*

Nothing, they're both Mooooooooooooooo ooooooooooooooody.

Oy, Henry, quit pretending to be me. I'm not putting in moody jokes, so there. I've got a much better idea.

**Oh yeah?**

Yeah. Ha ha ha.

# SUSAN'S SOUR JOKES

**SUSAN**: I always use
lemon juice for my complexion.
**MARGARET**: Maybe that's why you
always look so sour.

*What's the difference between Susan and Starbursts?*
Nothing. They're both sour.

**SUSAN**: Boys whisper they love me.
**HENRY**: Well, they wouldn't admit it out loud, would they?

Hey, I didn't write those!

**I wrote them for you, Susan - tee hee.**

*Who won the monster beauty contest?*
No one.

*They say Margaret is a raving beauty.*
You mean she's escaped from the funny farm?

Henry went into a joke store . . . and saw himself.

**You mean Susan went into a joke store . . .**

*Why are Susan and a snake alike?*
They're sssssssssour.

# MARGARET'S ABOMINABLE SNOWMAN JOKES

**Hey, that's not fair! Margaret should put in moody jokes NOT snowman jokes.**

Too bad, Henry! Now I'm sure to win. Vote Margaret!

*What did Jack Frost say to Frosty the Snowman?*
Have an ice day.

**PATIENT:** *Doctor, doctor, I keep thinking I'm a snowman.*
**DOCTOR:** *Keep cool.*

*Where does a snowman put his birthday candles?*
On his birthday flake.

*What do snowmen wear on their heads?*
Ice caps.

*What do you get if you cross a snowman and a shark?*
Frostbite.

*Where do snowmen put their webpages?*
On the winternet.

*What do snowmen call their offspring?*
Chill-dren.

*What happened when the icicle landed on the snowman's head?*
*It knocked him cold.*

*What did the snowman and his wife put over their baby's crib?*
A snowmobile.

*Where do snowmen go to dance?*
To snowballs.

*Why did a snowman send his father to Siberia?*
Because he wanted frozen pop.

*How does a snowman get to work?*
By icicle.

*What two letters of the alphabet do snowmen prefer?*
I.C.

*Where do snowmen keep their money?*
In a snowbank.

*What kind of money do snowmen use?*
Ice lolly.

# BOUDICCA'S BATTLE-AXE JOKES

*I have always had an excellent sense of humour, so I feel it is my duty to share some of my favourite jokes with you. Anyone who does not vote one of my jokes the best in the book will get four hours of homework a night.*

*What was the greatest accomplishment of the early Romans?*
Speaking Latin.

*Why does history keep repeating itself?*
Because we weren't listening the first time.

*What does a library book wear whenever it leaves the building?*
A pager.

*What did the executioner say to his mother?*
Only thirty chopping days to Christmas.

*Why are soldiers so tired on April 1st?*
They've just completed a 31 day March.

*What did one knife say to the other?*
Look sharp.

*What sort of star is dangerous?*
A shooting star.

*Who invented King Arthur's round table?*
Sir Cumference.

*When was King Arthur's army too tired to fight?*
When they had too many sleepless knights.

*Why did Henry VIII have so many wives?*
He liked to chop and change.

# TEACHER JOKES

**Pssst! Don't tell Miss Battle-Axe, but I've sneaked a few *real* teacher jokes into the book. Won't she get a shock!!!**

MISS BATTLE-AXE: *If 1+1=2 and 2+2=4, what is 4+4?*
HENRY: That's not fair! You answer the easy ones and leave us with the hard one.

MISS BATTLE-AXE: Order! Order!
HENRY: I'll have some chocolates and crisps.

**Henry:** Mum, I've got great news.
**Mum:** Did you pass your test?
**Henry:** Nah, but I was top of those who failed.

**Miss Battle-Axe:** What's 2 and 2?
**Clever Clare:** 4
**Miss Battle-Axe:** That's good.
**Clever Clare:** Good? That's perfect!

*What kind of food do maths teachers eat?*
Square meals.

**Miss Battle-Axe:** Well, at least there's one thing I can say about Henry.
**Dad:** What's that?
**Miss Battle-Axe:** With grades like these, he couldn't be cheating.

**Miss Battle-Axe:** What do you call a person who keeps on talking when people are no longer interested?
**Henry:** A teacher.

**Henry:** Hey Dad, can you write in the dark?
**Dad:** What do you want me to write?
**Henry:** Your name on this school report.

**Miss Battle-Axe:** If I had seven oranges in one hand and eight oranges in the other, what would I have?
**Horrid Henry:** Big hands.

**Mr Nerdon:** Ralph, why are you doing your maths sums on the floor?
**Rude Ralph:** You told me to do it without using tables.

**Miss Battle-Axe:** Henry, go to the map and find America.
**Henry:** Here it is.
**Miss Battle-Axe:** Correct. Now, class, who discovered America?
**Class:** Henry.

**Mrs Oddbod:** Why are you late?
**Sour Susan:** Because of the sign.
**Mrs Oddbod:** What sign?
**Sour Susan:** The one that says, 'School Ahead, Go Slow'.

**Miss Battle-Axe:** What's the chemical formula for water?
**Horrid Henry:** HIJKLMNO.
**Miss Battle-Axe:** What are you talking about?
**Horrid Henry:** Yesterday you said it's H to O.

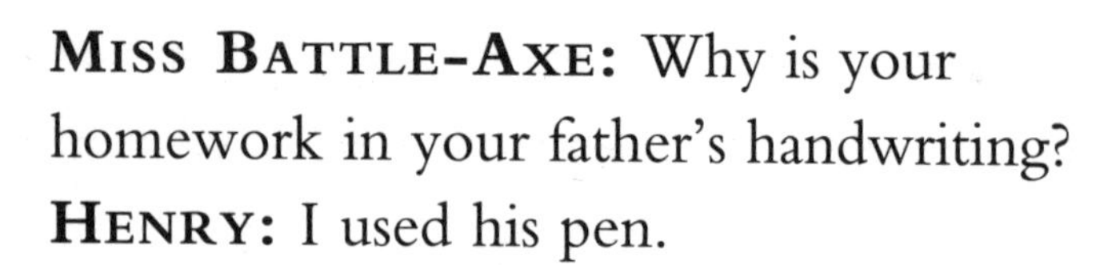

**Miss Battle-Axe:** Why is your homework in your father's handwriting?
**Henry:** I used his pen.

**Miss Battle-Axe:** How can you prevent diseases caused by biting insects?
**Clever Clare:** Don't bite any.

*Have you heard about the teacher who was cross-eyed?*
She couldn't control her pupils!

**Miss Battle-Axe:** Henry, your essay on 'My Cat' is exactly the same as Peter's. Did you copy his?
**Horrid Henry:** No, it's the same cat.

**Miss Battle-Axe:** Where is your homework?
**Henry:** I lost it fighting this kid who said you weren't the best teacher in the school.

**Now if that doesn't win the prize for me . . . tee hee!**

# LINDA'S LAZY JOKES

Yawn. I'm too tired to tell any jokes ...

*What should you do if you find a snake in your bed?*

Sleep in the wardrobe.

**LAZY LINDA:** I don't think my mum knows much about children.
**GORGEOUS GURINDER:** Why do you say that?
**LAZY LINDA:** Because she always puts me to bed when I'm wide awake, and gets me up when I'm sleepy.

*Why did the girl put her bed in the fireplace?*
Because she wanted to sleep like a log.

*How can you get breakfast in bed?*
Sleep in the kitchen.

*What's an undercover agent?*
A spy in bed.

*Where do books sleep?*
Under their covers.

*Why can't a bicycle stand up?*
Because it's too tired.

*Why shouldn't you believe a person in bed?*
Because he is lying.

*How do you get an alien baby to sleep?*
You rock-et.

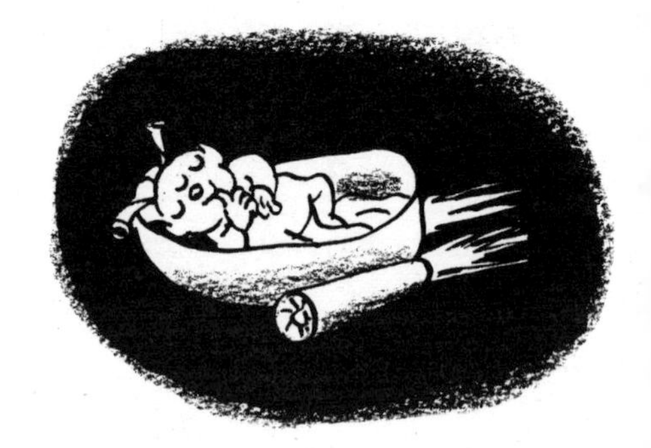

That's quite enough (yawn).

# GRAHAM'S GREEDY JOKES

C'mon everybody, vote for one of mine! I hear the prize is double your weight in sweets! And I don't get enough sweets.

I'm starving!

I need chocolate!

I need sweets!

I'm feeling weak from lack of sweets.

These jokes are making me hungry ...

Gimme sweeeeeets!!!!

*Knock! Knock!*
Who's there?
*Ice cream!*
Ice cream who?
*Ice cream if you throw*
*me in cold water.*

*Knock! Knock!*
Who's there?
*Ice cream soda.*
Icecreamsodawho?
*ICE CREAM SODA PEOPLE CAN*
*HEAR ME . . .*

*How do you make a cream puff?*
Chase it round the block.

*Knock knock.*
Who's there?
*Stew.*
Stew, who?
*Stew early to go to bed.*

*How do you fix a broken pizza?*
With tomato paste.

*How did the burger propose?*
With an onion ring.

*Why do hamburgers go to the gym?*
To get better buns.

*What are two things you can't have for lunch?*
Breakfast and dinner.

*What country did sweets come from?*
Sweeten.

*What did the cake say to the knife?*
You wanna piece of me?

*What did the nut say when it sneezed?*
Cashew.

*What do you get if you cross a snake with a pie?*
A pie-thon.

*What do Italian monsters eat?*
Spook-ghetti.

*What is a pie's favorite sport?*
Pie Kwan Do.

*What did the teddy bear say when he was offered dessert?*
No thanks, I'm stuffed!

## THE FAMILY OF TOMATOES

A family of three tomatoes were walking in town one day when the baby tomato started lagging behind.

The big father tomato walked back to the baby tomato, stomped on her, and said, 'Ketchup!'

*What do you get when you cross a cocoa bean with an elk?*
Chocolate moose.

*Where did the spaghetti go to dance?*
The meat-ball.

*What's yellow and stupid?*
Thick custard.

*What do you call two banana peels?*
A pair of slippers.

*Waiter, waiter, this soup tastes funny.*
Well, you did ask for something with a little body in it.

*Why is 't' so important to a stick insect?*
Because without it, it would be a sick insect.

*Why did the banana go out with the prune?*
He couldn't find a date.

*What is yellow and white, and throws itself off the edge of the dining table?*
A lemming meringue.

These jokes are making me starving! Vote Graham. I need sweets.

# MARTHA'S MAGIC JOKES

*Abracadabra, hocus pocus, when I count to three, you will all vote for me . . .*

**Nice try, Martha. But you can't beat my pirate jokes!**

*What happened to the magic tractor?*
It went down the lane and turned into a field.

**Miss Battle-Axe:** What's your father's job?
**Magic Martha:** He's a magician.
**Miss Battle-Axe:** How interesting. What's his favourite trick?
**Magic Martha:** He saws people in half.
**Miss Battle-Axe:** Goodness. Do you have any brothers of sisters?
**Magic Martha:** One half brother and two half sisters.

*Why can't the magician tell his magic secrets in the garden?*
The corn has ears and the potatoes have eyes.

*How did the magician cut the sea in half?*
With a sea saw.

*What do a footballer and a magician have in common?*
Both do hat tricks.

You will all vote for me, you will all vote for me, you will all vote for me . . .

# WILLIAM'S WEEPY JOKE

Waaaaahhh! I wanted to tell my joke first . . .

*Why was the cookie crying?*
Because its mother had been a wafer so long.

Waaaahhh! Nobody laughed at my joke . . .

# SORAYA'S SINGING JOKES

Tra la la la la. Do re mi fa so la ti do. Do ti la so fa–

**Oh shut up Soraya!**

Miss Battle-Axe! Henry told me to shut up!

*Don't be horrid, Henry, or I'll remove your jokes from the book.*

**Huh. She wouldn't dare . . .**

*What's the most musical part of a turkey?*
The drumstick.

*Why can't skeletons sing in church?*
Because they've got no organs.

*What do you call a musical automobile?*
A car—toon.

*What is a monster's favourite song?*
Ghouls just want to have fun.

*What kind of music does a mummy listen to?*
Wrap music.

*Why did Miss Thumper get locked in a classroom?*
Because her keys were in the piano.

*What's green and sings?*
Elvis Parsley.

*What's the most musical bone?*
The trom-bone.

*What's the wettest animal in the world?*
Reindeer.

*What sugar sings?*
Icing sugar.

*Why did Mozart sell his sheep?*
Because they wouldn't stop saying, 'Bach! Bach!'

# RALPHS'S RUDE JOKES

Oh boy, stop reading now, all you prissy toads. These jokes are so rude–

**Hey, that's not fair! I want to tell the rude jokes!**

Too bad, Henry, I got here first.

**I order you to stop. These are *my* jokes.**

No way!

**I told Ralph all these jokes anyway. So really they count as mine.**

*What did one toilet say to the other?*
You look a bit flushed.

*Why did Peter take toilet paper to the party?*
Because he was a party pooper.

**Hey, Ralph! That's really funny.**

No it isn't! Mum! Miss Lovely! Ralph called me a party pooper!

**Shut up, tell-tale.**

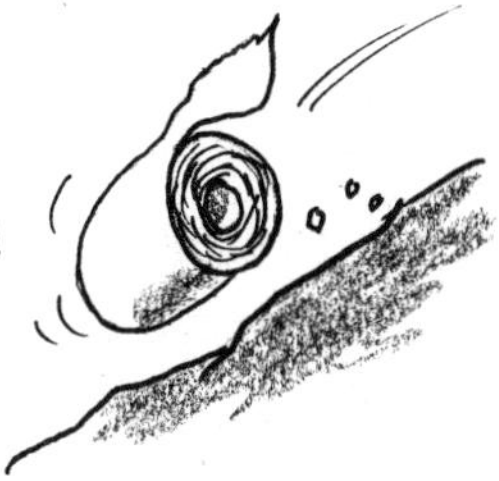

*Why did the toilet roll roll down the hill?*
It wanted to get to the bottom.

*Why do boys have spots?*
So they can play dot to dot.

*What did the toilet roll say to the other toilet roll?*
People keep ripping me off.

*Doctor, doctor, I've got a sore throat.*
So go over to the window and stick your tongue out.
*Why will that help?*
It won't. I just don't like my neighbours.

*What tree can't you climb?*
A lavatory.

*What colour is a burp?*
Burple.

*What do you call a fairy who hasn't taken a bath?*
Stinkerbell.

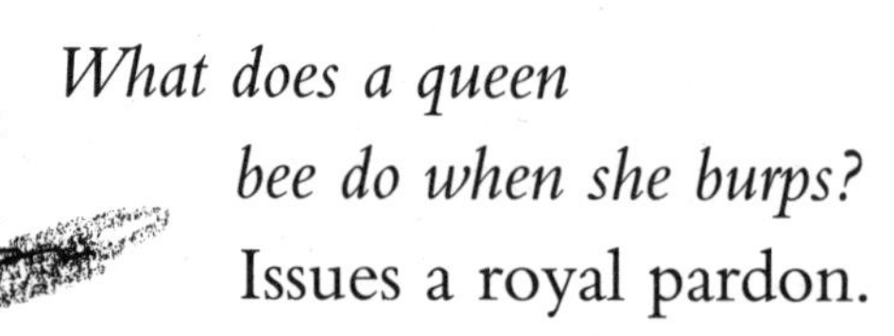

*What does a queen bee do when she burps?*
Issues a royal pardon.

*Did you ever see the movie 'Constipated'?*
It never came out.

*What did the judge say when the skunk walked into the courtroom?*
Odour in the court.

*How do you know when a dog has been naughty?*
It leaves a little poodle on the carpet.

*What did one eye say to the other eye?*
Just between you and me . . . something smells.

*What's brown and sounds like a bell?*
Dung.

*Knock knock.*
Who's there?
*The interrupting sheep.*
The interrupting sh—
**BAAAAAA!**

*What do you get if you cross Henry and Margaret?*
A mess.

**That is so not funny, Ralph!**
Yes it is, Henry.
**Is not!**

Is too!

**Okay, what do you get if you cross Ralph and Margaret? A big mess.**

That is so not funny, Henry!

# AL'S AEROBIC JOKES

**One-two, one-two, one-two, c'mon you lazy lumps, get out there, shake a leg, run ten miles, do some press-ups, climb a mountain, swim the Atlantic . . . Stop lying about! Put down this book and go for a run!**

*How do athletes stay cool during a game?*
They stand near the fans.

*Which sport is always in trouble?*
Bad-minton.

*What did the two strings do in the race?*
They tied.

**AEROBIC AL:** Is your refrigerator running?
**GREEDY GRAHAM:** Yeah.
**AEROBIC AL:** Well you'd better go catch it.

*What time of year do you jump on a trampoline?*
Springtime.

*When is cricket a crime?*
When there's a hit and run.

*Where do spiders play football?*
Webley.

*What do runners do when they forget something?*
They jog their memory.

**Now c'mon, you lazy lumps, vote for me! (Then run up and down the stairs one hundred times.)**

# PETER'S PERFECT JOKES

These are the best jokes in the world, and I know you will all love them. Please vote for one of my jokes.

Peter.

**What? These are the dumbest jokes ever! Anyone who reads them will get thrown into a snake pit. Do not read unless you want everyone to know you're a toad.**

*Knock knock.*
Who's there?
*Ya.*
Yahoo!

*Knock knock.*
Who's there?
*Doctor.*
Doctor Who?
*You just said.*

*Knock knock.*
Who's there?
*Leaf.*
Leaf who?
*Leaf me alone.*

**These jokes are so lame. Take my advice and skip over them.**

*How do you make a witch itch?*
Take away the W.

*What did the traffic light say to the man crossing the road?*
Don't look, I'm changing!

*Who invented the plane that didn't fly?*
The Wrong Brothers.

*What did one earthquake say to another?*
It's not my fault.

*Who writes invisible books?*
A ghost writer.

*What is a myth?*
A female moth.

**I said anyone who is not a toad should skip over these 'jokes'.**

*Knock Knock.*
Who's there?
*Cats go.*
Cats go who?
*No they don't, they go meow!!!!!!*

**Groan.**

*What kind of underwear do clouds wear?*
Thunderwear.

**Henry:** What's that terrible, ugly thing on your shoulder?
**Peter:** Help! What is it?
**Henry:** Your head.

Miss Lovely! Henry's being mean to me! He's adding jokes on my page!

*Henry! Cross that joke out immediately.*

**But it's a great joke. I'm only trying to help Peter . . .**

*What nut grows on a wall?*
A walnut.

*What did the wall say to the corner?*
Meet you at the ceiling.

*Where does Tarzan get his clothes from?*
A jungle sale.

**You are a toad, you are a toad . . .**

Waaaaa! Henry's calling me a toad.

*Stop it Henry.*

*What do you call an overweight pumpkin?*
A plumpkin.

***What has three heads, is ugly, and smells bad?***
**Oops, my mistake, you don't have three heads!**

Waaaaaa! Miss Lovely! He did it again! He stuck another joke on my page.

*What is the best day to go to the beach?*
*Sunday, of course.*

*What does a teddy bear put in his house?*
Fur-niture.

*What city cheats at exams?*
Peking.

**I guess you must like snake pits. Oh, okay, you didn't read them, you just skipped through them to the end. Phew. You had me worried there for a minute.**

# BERT'S BEEFY BEASTLY JOKES

**PETER:** Why did the chicken cross the road?
**BERT:** I dunno.

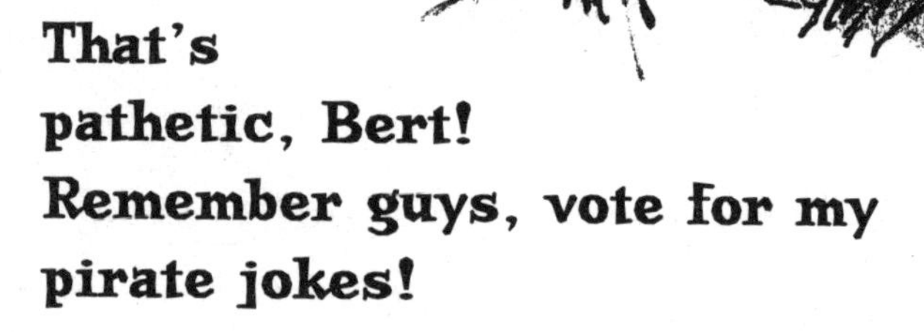


*Where do cows go on a Saturday night?*
To the mooooooovies.

*What do you get when you cross a rotten egg with a giant gorilla?*
King Pong.

## *I* think you get . . . PETER!

Miss Lovely!! Henry's still writing mean things about me in the new joke book.

*Stop it, Henry, or no playtime.*

*Knock knock.*

Who's there?

*Cows.*

Cows who?

*Cows say moo, not who.*

*What do you call a dog that tells time?*

A watch dog.

*What newspaper do cats read?*

Mews of the World.

*Why don't baby birds smile?*
Would you like it if your mother fed you worms all day?

*What's the difference between a bird and a fly?*
A bird can fly but a fly can't bird.

*What has an elephant's trunk, a tiger's stripes, a giraffe's neck, and a baboon's bottom?*
A zoo.

*What do you get if you cross an owl with a skunk?*
A bird that smells but doesn't give a hoot.

*What happened to the snake with a cold?*
She adder viper nose.

*What's the best year for kangaroos?*
Leap year.

*What did the porcupine say to the cactus?*
Mummy.

*What do you call a three legged donkey?*
A wonkey.

*What do you give a sick bird?*
Tweetment.

*What is green and goes dit dot dit dot?*
A morse toad.

*What do you call a frog spy?*
A croak and dagger agent.

*Why does an elephant wear plimsolls?*
To sneak up on mice.

*What has four legs and flies?*
A dead horse.

*Why did the fly fly?*
Because the spider spied her.

*What do you get from a pampered cow?*
Spoiled milk.

*What weighs six tons and wears glass slippers?*
Cinder-elephant.

*Where do polar bears vote?*
The North Poll.

*Where was Camelot?*
A place where people parked their camels.

*What do you get when you cross a lizard and a baby?*
A creepy crawler.

*What did the spider do on the computer?*
Made a website.

*What do moths study in school?*
Mothomatics.

*What card game do crocodiles play?*
Snap!

**Aren't you going to ask people to vote for you, Bert?**

I dunno.

# CLARE'S CLEVER JOKES

Not everyone can be as smart as me, but have a go at these clever conundrums. Oh, and please vote for one of my brain teasers.

*What is the world's longest word?*
Smiles, because there's a mile between the first and second 's'.

*Why is the sky so high?*
So birds don't bump their heads.

*What do you get when you cross a pair of pants with a dictionary?*
Smarty pants.

*When can a donkey be spelled in one letter?*
When it's you.

*What type of snake is good at sums?*
An adder.

*Why was 6 afraid of 7?*
Because 7 8 9.

*What holds the moon up?*
Moon beams.

*What breaks when you say it?*
Silence.

*What loses its head in the morning and gets it back at night?*
Your pillow.

*What's harder to catch the faster you run?*
Your breath.

**Don't forget to vote for Clever Clare.**

# BRIAN'S BRAINY RIDDLES

Now come on, all you geniuses out there! Try these riddles, and then show how brainy you are by voting for me.

*What's bigger when it's upside down?*
The number 6.

*What has a mouth, and a fork, but never eats?*
A river.

*What's in the middle of Paris?*

R.

*How many sides has a circle got?*

Two – the inside and the outside.

*What's black when clean and white when dirty?*

A blackboard.

*What has a tail and a head but no body?*

A coin.

*What room has no sides, no walls, no doors, and no ceilings?*

A mushroom.

*What gets wet as it dries?*
A towel.

*What has two hands and no fingers?*
A clock.

*What starts with a T, ends with a T, and is full of tea?*
A teapot.

*What asks no questions, but demands an answer?*
The doorbell.

*Twelve pears hanging high, twelve men passing by, each took a pear and left eleven hanging there. How can this be? How can eleven pears be left?*
'Each' is a man's name!

**Brian is a brain! Vote Brainy Brian.**

# HENRY'S PURPLE HAND PIRATE JOKES

Okay everybody, finally, you are now going to read the best jokes in the book!! Can I help it if mine are so much better than everyone else's? Get your pencils ready to vote . . .

Henry!

*Why are pirates called pirates?*
Because they aaarrrrr!

*What does a pirate smoke?*
A cigaaaarrrrrr!

*What does a pirate's dog say?*
Aaaarrrrrf!

*What do pirates get on their pizzas?*
Arrrrrrtichokes!

*What does a Dyslexic Pirate Say?*
RRRRAAAAAAAAAA!

*Where do Pirates hate to be kicked?*
In the ARRRse!

*Why does a pirate's phone go beep beep beep beep beep?*
Because he left it off the hook.

*What's a pirate's favourite letter?*
P. Because it's an R, but it's missing a leg!

*What do you get when you cross a pirate with Santa Claus?*
Yo ho ho ho!

*What has 8 legs, 8 arms and 8 eyes?*
8 pirates.

*How much do pirates pay for their earrings?*
A buccaneer.

*Why did Captain Hook cross the road?*
To get to the second hand shop.

**Remember: vote often, for . . . Henry!!**

# HORRID HENRY'S LAST LAUGH

**Shh, don't tell, I've sneaked in a few practical jokes. Don't let Miss Battle-Axe know!!!!!**

1) Did you know that if you mix shampoo with grass and leave it on the floor, Mum and Dad will think the cat threw up?

2) Carry a piece of old cloth with you. Wait till your victim sits down or bends over, then rip it behind their back. They will be so embarrassed!!!

3) Don't forget about putting salt in the sugar bowl . . .

4) Want to give your yucky sister or revolting brother a fright? One weekend, move their clock ahead three hours. When they wake up, they'll think they over-slept!

5) Psst, here's a quick way to make some cash. Tell your silly sister or brother: 'Bet you I can push myself under the door.' When they accept the bet, write MYSELF on a piece of paper and push it under the door. Collect your well-earned cash!

6) Ask your horrible, smelly brother or sister:

*If frozen water is iced water, and frozen lemonade is iced lemonade, what's frozen ink?*

# HORRID HENRY'S MIGHTY JOKE BOOK

For my very own Jolly Josh

# CONTENTS

# HORRID HENRY'S MIGHTY JOKE BOOK

Isn't that typical? You have the brilliant, wonderful, spectacular idea of writing a joke book, and then suddenly EVERYONE wants to do it. What they don't know is that I saved my best horrid jokes. And my best skeleton jokes. And my best school jokes. This joke book is ALL mine! I can do whatever I want! Which means I get to keep *all* the money!!! No more sharing!

Because I have had a brilliant, spectacular idea. I'll charge everybody hundreds of pounds to have their name in my book.

Then I'll charge them hundreds of pounds to *buy* the book. I'm going to buy 30 TVs and 5 computers and the Frosty Freeze ice cream factory.

And since I've chosen the very best jokes for a few friends (and evil enemies) they'll be sure to buy loads of copies!

# JOSH'S JOLLY JOKES

**If you don't laugh out loud at Josh's jolly jokes I'll—I'll—I'll give Peter £3. Actually make that £1. No, 25p. Hmm, wait, I have a better idea. I'll make Peter give *me* 50p every time you laugh. So get laughing.**

*Why was the computer cold?*
It forgot to close its windows.

*What did the hungry computer say?*
I could go for a byte.

*Who is Snow White's brother?*
Egg white. Get the yolk?

*Where is*
*Captain*
*Hook's*
*treasure chest?*
Under his treasure shirt.

*What did one shoelace*
*say to the other shoelace?*
That's knot mine.

*Why did Mrs Grape leave Mr Grape?*
She was tired of raisin kids.

*Why couldn't the sailors play cards?*
Because the captain was on the deck.

*What do jokes and pencils have in common?*
They're no good without a point.

*What will they do when the Forth Bridge collapses?*
Build a fifth bridge.

*What do you say to a chicken before a performance?*
Break an egg.

*Why shouldn't you play cards in the jungle?*
There are too many cheetahs.

*What do you call a naughty monkey?*
A badboon.

*Why did the fly go to Paris?*
He wanted to become a French fly.

*Why do chickens watch television?*
For hen-tertainment.

*What do you use to fix a broken tooth?*
Toothpaste.

*Do you know me?*
Yes.
*Knock knock.*
Who's there?
*I thought you knew me.*

*How does an Eskimo build his house?*
Igloos it together.

*What monster dances the best?*
The bogey man.

*What can make grass grow bigger?*
Magnifying Grass.

*Why does a cow moo?*
Because its horns don't work.

*Knock knock.*
Who's there?
*Too whit.*
Too whit who?
*Is there an owl in the house?*

*What was Humpty Dumpty wearing when he fell?*
A shellsuit.

*Knock knock.*
Who's there?
*Turner.*
Turner who?
*Turner round there's a monster.*

*Why do birds fly south?*
Because it's too far to walk.

*Knock knock.*
Who's there?
*Chile.*
Chile who?
*Chile being an abominable snowman.*

# KATE'S KUNG-FU JOKES

**I'll keep well away from Kate and her kung-fu chops when she reads these magnificent martial arts jokes. Haiiiiiii-ya!**

*What happened when the karate champion joined the army and saluted?*

He nearly killed himself.

*What lives in a pod and is a kung-fu expert?*
Bruce pea.

*Why are the Olympic qualifiers in kung-fu so hot?*
Because there is hardly a fan in the place.

*What do you get when you cross a karate expert with a pig?*
Pork chops.

*What does a martial arts fan eat?*
Kung food.

*Why was the sword swallower sent to prison?*
He coughed and killed two people.

# VIOLET'S VAIN JOKES

Henry, do I get to see my jokes before you put them in?

**Violet, I'm insulted. You'll love the jokes, promise. Now pay up.**

*Why did Violet join the Navy?*
So the world could see her.

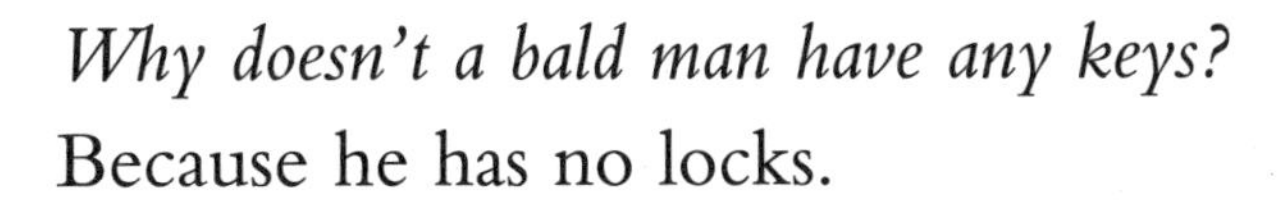

*Why doesn't a bald man have any keys?*
Because he has no locks.

*What do you call a very popular perfume?*
A best-smeller.

**Violet:** Is that perfume I smell?
**Margaret:** It is, and yes, you do.

**Violet:** I'm all red and blistered from sitting in the sun.
**Henry:** Well, I guess you basked for it.

**Violet:** Did you see me at the beauty contest?
**Henry:** On and off.
**Violet:** How did you like me?
**Henry:** Off.

*Why couldn't the athlete listen to her music?*
Because she'd broken a record.

*Where can you play elastic guitar?*
In a rubber band.

*What instrument goes 'ring ring'?*
A saxo-phone.

*What kind of music do balloons hate?*
Pop.

*How do you make a bandstand?*
Take their chairs away.

*How do you clean a flute?*
With a tuba toothpaste.

*What is Beethoven doing in his grave?*
De-composing.

*What food is essential to good music?*
Beets.

*Why did the music teacher need a ladder?*
To reach the high notes.

*Where did the music teacher leave her keys?*
In the piano.

*How do you get cool music?*
Put your CDs in the fridge.

*What is a rabbit's favourite dance style?*
Hip hop.

*Why was the musician arrested?*
Because he got in treble.

*What makes music on your head?*
A head band.

*What is the loudest pet?*
The trum-pet.

*What is a computer's favourite music?*
Disc-o.

*What is Tarzan's favourite Christmas song?*
Jungle-Bells.

# THE QUEEN'S QUEENLY JOKES

**Now that I've met the queen (and you haven't - ha ha) I thought I'd put in a few jokes for her. Then she can buy a copy of this book for a million pounds. In fact, if she bought 5 copies, that'd be £5 million for me. Whoopee!**

*Why did the queen draw straight lines?*
Because she was the ruler.

*Why did the queen go to the dentist?*
To get her teeth crowned.

*How do you find King Arthur in the dark?*
With a knight light.

*Knock Knock*
Who's there?
*Neil.*
Neil who?
*Neil down before the queen.*

*What kind of wood is a queen?*

A ruler.

# IAN'S INKY JOKES

**Ian wants to be a writer when he grows up, so this is to make sure he makes *me* the hero of his books.**

*What did the pen say to the pencil?*
What's your point?

*What do you get when you cross a library and an elf?*
A shhh—elf.

*What has a spine but no bones?*
A book.

*What's the difference between a boring teacher and a boring book?*

You can shut the book up.

*What do young ghosts write their homework in?*

Exorcise books.

*Who makes the best bookkeepers?*

People who borrow your books and don't return them.

*How do you start writing a book about ducks?*

With an intro-duck-tion.

*What did one pencil say to the other?*

You're looking sharp.

# TED'S TIDY JOKES

**Oh no, no way, get away from me, Ted, your stupid smelly baby jokes will appear in my book over my dead body. No chance, toad, so get out of – What's that? You'll pay £2 for every joke I include? Well, well, Ted, my friend, step right up, it will be a pleasure to include your jokes.**

*What did the mummy broom say to the baby broom?*
It's time to go to sweep.

**Ted, gimme £3 or that joke is out.**

*Where does a broom go when it's tired?*
It goes to sweep.

**Make that £5 - your jokes are awful.**

*Why do witches fly on broomsticks?*
Because Hoovers are too heavy.

*Why was the broom late?*
He over-swept.

**That does it. £7 cold hard cash - or else.**

*What can't be untied?*
A rainbow.

*How does a vampire clean his house?*
With a victim cleaner.

*Have you heard the joke about the dustbin?*
Well don't listen, it's a load of rubbish.

**The things I do for money . . .**

# PETER'S PERFECT JOKES

Mum! Henry's trying to make me pay him for putting my jokes in the joke book.

Henry!
Don't be horrid.

**Peter has pouffy pants, Peter has pouffy pants.**

Muuuuuuuuum!

Henry, this is your final warning. Be nice to Peter or no TV for a week.

**Humph. It's so unfair.**

**Psst, everybody, just skip these rotten jokes. Just 'cause I put them in doesn't mean you have to read them. Sometimes you have to make sacrifices for cold, hard, cash.**

*Who stole the soap?*
The robber ducky.

**See what I mean?**

*Why did the belt go to jail?*
Because it held up some trousers.

**Of all the brothers in the world, I had to get him . . .**

*What do you get when you cross a camera with a mouse?*
Cheese.

*How do hedgehogs play leapfrog?*
Very carefully.

*What happens if you eat yeast and shoe polish?*
Every morning you'll rise and shine.

*What did the snail say when he was riding on the tortoise's back?*
Wheeeeee!

**Groan.**

*Where did Noah keep his bees on the Ark?*
In the arc-hives.

**Remember, everyone, Peter's jokes have nothing to do with me.**

*What was the snail doing on the motorway?*
A couple of miles a week.

**Peter! That's so dumb!**

Isn't!

**Is. Pay me an extra £2.**

No! Muuuuuuuuum!
Henry's being mean to me.

**Shut up, Peter.**

You shut up, Henry.

# Muuuuuuuum!

**Peter told me to shut up.**

# Muuuuuuuuum!

Henry told me to shut up.

**Did not!**

Did too!

*What kind of flower grows on your face?*
Tulips.

**Stop! Stop! That's enough terrible jokes.**

**Stop! Emergency! Help!!! Bad joke alert! Danger! Danger!**

**Phew. He's finished. Panic over.**

# AL'S AEROBIC JOKES

**Al says I owe him loads of cash which is completely not true because he ate more of the sweets than I did, but – okay, I'll let him put in a few sporty jokes for free.**

*What's the hardest part about sky-diving?*
The ground.

*What's a golfer's favourite letter?*
Tee

*How can you make an apple puff?*
Chase it round the garden.

*Why should bowling alleys be quiet?*
So you can hear a pin drop.

*How long does it take for a gymnast to get to class?*
A split second.

*Which sport is always in trouble?*
Bad-minton.

*What does the winner of a race lose?*
Her breath.

*What's a horse's favourite sport?*
Stable tennis.

*What animal is best at hitting a baseball?*
A bat.

*Why does a wrestler bring a key to the match?*
To get out of a headlock.

*Why do basketball players love biscuits?*
Because they can dunk them.

*What drink do wrestlers like?*
Fruit punch.

*Why is it so hot in a football stadium after a match?*
Because all the fans have left.

*When is cricket a crime?*
When there's a hit and run.

*Why can't you tell a joke while ice-skating?*
The ice might crack up.

# FLUFFY'S FLUFFY JOKES

**Mum said I had to let the family contribute to the book. And Fluffy's family, right? I'd rather have Fluffy's jokes than Peter's, any day.**

*What's yellow and hops up and down?*
A canary with hiccups.

*What does a cat go to sleep on?*
A catterpillow.

*What's big and hairy and flies at 1200 miles per hour?*
King Kongcorde.

**HENRY:** Where do fleas go in winter?
**FLUFFY:** Search me.

*What kind of cats love water?*
Octopusses.

*What are cats' favourite animals?*
Mice.

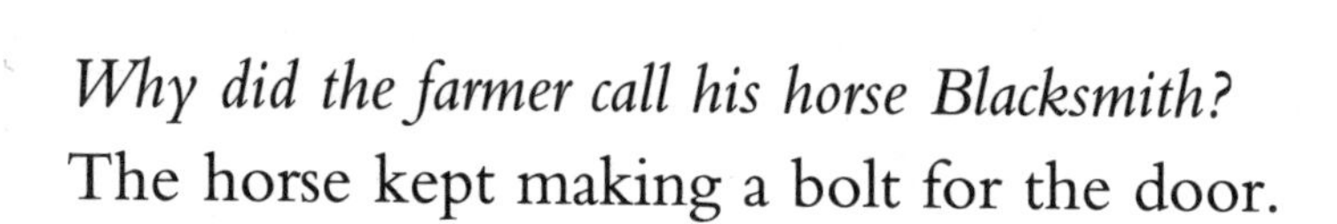

*Why did the farmer call his horse Blacksmith?*
The horse kept making a bolt for the door.

*What's Fluffy's favourite colour?*
Puurrrple.

Two cows are in a field. One says 'moo' and the other says 'I was just going to say that.'

*What do you get if you cross an elephant with a kangaroo?*
Holes all over Australia.

*Why do fish live in salt water?*
Because pepper makes them sneeze.

*How do you make a goldfish age?*
Take out the 'g'.

*Why did the cat get arrested?*
Because of the kitty litter.

*How does a dog say how?*
He howls!

*What do you call a dog on a beach?*
A hot dog.

*What do you call an elephant that flies?*
A jumbo jet.

Two cats were crossing
the English Channel:
One, Two, Three and
Un, Deux, Trois. Which one won?
One, Two, Three, because Un, Deux,
Trois, Quatre Cinq!

# NICK'S NEW OPERA JOKES

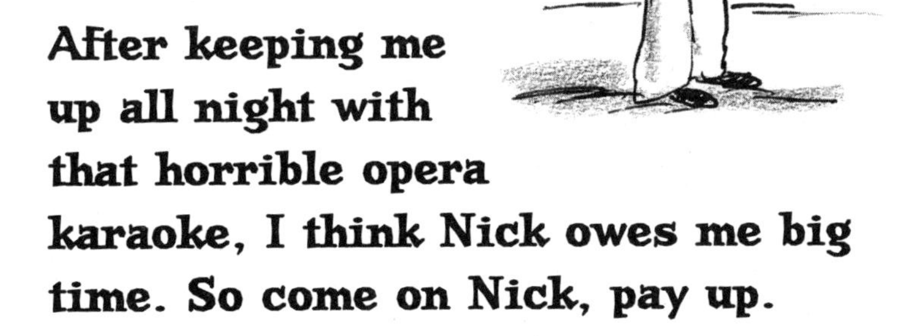

**After keeping me up all night with that horrible opera karaoke, I think Nick owes me big time. So come on Nick, pay up.**

Ok Henry, I'll give you £1 if you put in a joke for me.

**£1? To put a joke in my fabulous joke book? No way.**

All right, seven jokes. And I'll buy a copy to give to my sister for her birthday.

**Nick, it will be a pleasure to include your jokes. (I'm rich!!!!!)**

*How many sopranos does it take to change a lightbulb?*
Three. One to do it, one to understudy her, and one to say she could have done it better.

*How many tenors does it take to change a lightbulb?*
Three. One to do it,
and two to say it's too high for him.

*How do you save a tenor from drowning?*
Take your foot off his head.

*Why did the opera singer have such a high voice?*
She had falsetto teeth.

*What's the difference between a soprano and a piranha?*
Lipstick.

*What's a snake's favourite opera?*
Wriggleto.

# MRS ODDBOD'S ODD JOKES

**Tee hee. I think I'll collect the cash from Mrs Oddbod *before* I let her read these teacher jokes. Tell them to *your* teacher at your own risk!!!!**

**MRS ODDBOD:** Will any idiots in the room please stand up? (Henry stood.)

**MRS ODDBOD:** Henry, why do you think you're an idiot?

**HENRY**: Actually I don't, but I hate to see you standing there all by yourself.

*Why did Miss Lovely have to wear sunglasses?*
Because her pupils were so bright.

*What happened when Miss Battle-Axe tied the class's shoelaces together?*
They went on a class trip.

*What happened to the plant in Henry's maths class?*
It grew square roots.

*How do bees get to school?*
On the school buzz.

*Why was the clock sent to Mrs Oddbod's office?*

Because he was tocking too much.

*What do you get if you cross Miss Battle-Axe with a horoscope?*

A horrorscope.

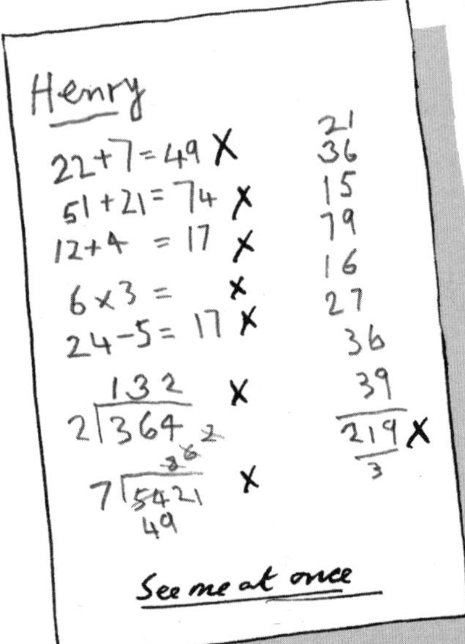


**MUM:** Does Miss Battle-Axe like you?

**HENRY:** Like me? She loves me! Look at all those Xs on my test paper.

**RUDE RALPH** (on the phone): My son has a bad cold and won't be able to come to school today.
**SCHOOL SECRETARY:** Who's this?
**RALPH:** This is my dad speaking.

**MISS BATTLE-AXE:** Henry, what are you going to be when you leave school?
**HENRY:** An old man.

**MISS BATTLE-AXE:** Henry, you aren't paying attention to me. Are you having trouble hearing?
**HENRY:** No, I'm having trouble listening.

# MUM'S MUMMY JOKES

**I've put Mum down for 150 books, so that's her Christmas shopping solved.**

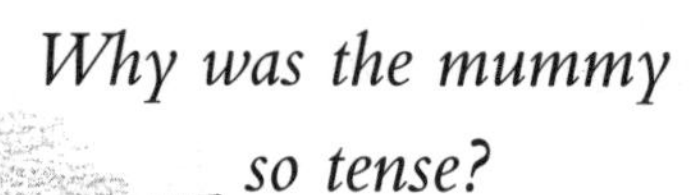

*Why was the mummy so tense?*

She was all wound up.

*What kind of girl does a mummy take on a date?*

Anyone he can dig up.

*Why did the mummy leave her tomb after 1,000 years?*
Because she thought she was old enough to leave home.

*What are a mummy's two favourite kinds of music?*
Ragtime and wrap.

*How can you tell if a mummy has a cold?*
He starts coffin.

*Why couldn't the mummy come outside?*
Because he was all wrapped up.

How do mummies hide?
*They wear masking tape.*

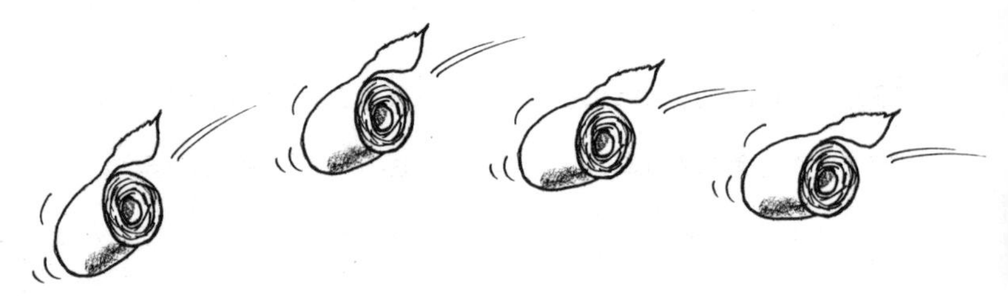

*Why don't mummies take vacations?*
They're afraid they'll relax and unwind.

*What did Tutankhamun say when he got scared?*
I want my mummy.

# DR DETTOL'S DOCTOR JOKES

**Dr Dettol owes me some cash after that mean trick she played on me with that injection . . .**

*What did the doctor give the patient with a splitting headache?*
Glue.

*Why was the doctor always angry?*
Because he had no patients.

*Why did the window see the doctor?*
He was having window panes.

A woman poisoned herself last week eating a daffodil bulb. The doctors told her she would be all right and will be out in the spring.

*What does the dentist call her x-rays?*
Tooth-pics.

*How many psychiatrists does it take to change a lightbulb?*
Just one, but the lightbulb has to really want to change.

*Why did the banana go to the doctor?*
Because it wasn't peeling very well.

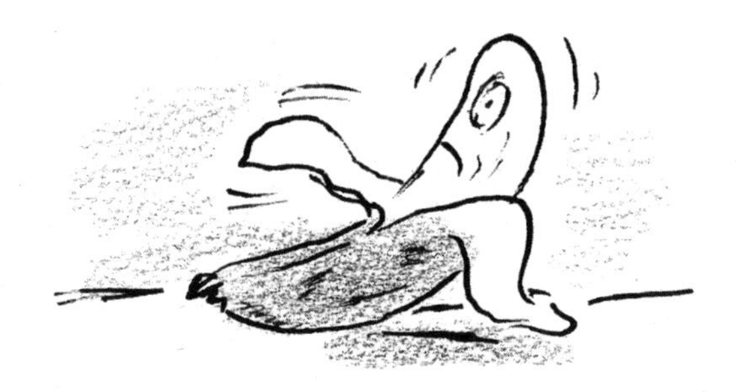

*Why are fish so easy to weigh?*
Because they have their own scales.

*Who do fish go to see when they're not feeling well?*
The Doctopus.

# SID'S SOGGY JOKES

**Hmmn, Soggy Sid, world's worst swimming teacher. Still, I'm sure he'll want to contribute to this great cause, 'Save a child'– I just won't mention that *I'm* the child . . .**

*In which direction does a chicken swim?*
Cluck-wise.

*What is a polar bear's favourite stroke?*
Blubber-fly.

*Why did Miss Battle-Axe jump into the pool?*
She wanted to test the water.

*Why wasn't Sour Susan scared when she went swimming and saw a shark?*
Because it was a *man*-eating shark.

*Why can elephants swim whenever they want?*
They always have their *trunks* with them.

# DR JEKYLL'S SPOOKY JOKES

**Scaredy-cats beware! Don't read these jokes when you are all alone, it's dark out, and there's a strange, scratching noise coming from inside the—**

*What do you do with a green monster?*
Wait until it ripens.

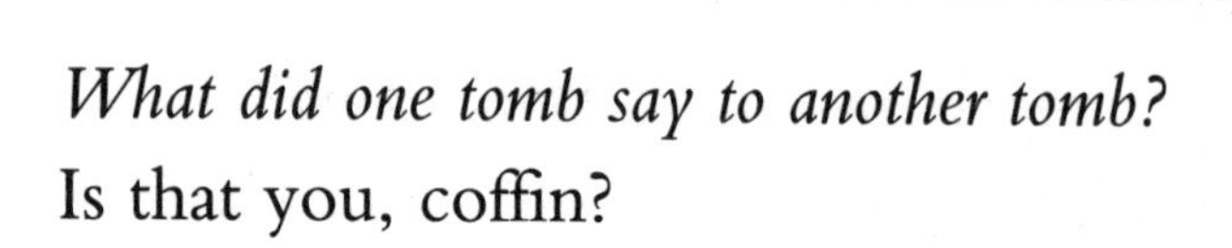


*What did one tomb say to another tomb?*
Is that you, coffin?

*What's the scariest position on a football team?*
Ghoulie.

*What subject did the witch get an A+ in?*
Spell-ing.

*Why was there thunder and lightning in the lab?*

The scientists were brainstorming.

*Where does Dracula stay in New York?*
The Vampire State Building.

*How many ears did Captain Kirk have?*
Three: a left ear, a right ear and a final frontier.

*Which vampire tried to eat James Bond?*
Ghouldfinger.

*What's the first thing that vampires learn at school?*
The alphabat.

*Why did the vampire enjoy ballroom dancing?*
Because he loved the vaultz.

*What's a vampire's favourite food?*
Scream of mushroom.

*What is Dracula's favourite fruit?*

Neck-tarines.

*What's a vampire's favourite animal?*

A giraffe.

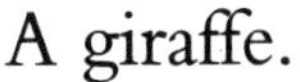

*Why was the vampire thin?*

He ate necks to nothing.

*What do zombies eat with bread and cheese?*

Pickled organs.

# GRETA'S GREASY JOKES

**Demon dinner-ladies beware!**
**These yucky food jokes will send everyone screaming from lunch.**

*What's the best thing to put in a pie?*
Your teeth.

*What did one crisp say to the other?*
Want to go for a dip?

*What's green and round and goes camping?*
A boy sprout.